Aberdeenshire Library and Information Service
www.aberdeenshire.gov.uk/libraries
Renewals Hotline 01224 661511

22 MAR 2013	-5 FEB 2019	15 FEB 2020
HQ	-9 MAR 2019	21 FEB 2022
-6 JUN 2013	23 APR 2019	
26 JUN 2013		16 JUN 2022
21 AUG 2013	-6 MAY 2019	0 NOV 2023
C5 MAR 2014	-6 AUG 2019	09 DEC 2023
HQ	02 SEP 2019	
13 MAR 2014	-4 OCT 2019	
27 NOV 2017	12 NOV 2019	
	16 DEC 2019	ABERDEENSHIRE LIBRARIES
0 1 NOV 2018		WITHDRAWN FROM LIBRARY
30 NOV 2022		

SMALLMAN, Clive

D1576722

ABERDEENSHIRE LIBRARIES

1916575

To my dad, thanks for everything! – S S

For my dad, Phillip 'Juggy' Julian – S J

JP

LITTLE TIGER PRESS
An imprint of Magi Publications
1 The Coda Centre, 189 Munster Road, London SW6 6AW
www.littletigerpress.com
First published in Great Britain 2012
Text copyright © Steve Smallman 2012 • Illustrations copyright © Sean Julian 2012
Steve Smallman and Sean Julian have asserted their rights to be
identified as the author and illustrator of this work under
the Copyright, Designs and Patents Act, 1988
A CIP catalogue record for this book is
available from the British Library
All rights reserved
ISBN 978-1-84895-317-8
Printed in China
LTP/1400/0297/1011

2 4 6 8 10 9 7 5 3 1

My Dad!

Steve Smallman   Sean Julian

LITTLE TIGER PRESS
London

Some dads will give you **enormous** great cuddles.

Some dads join in when you're **jumping** in *puddles*.

Some dads will run up
and down by your side,
Holding your bike till you
learn how to ride.

Some dads can cheer you up
when you are crying,

And hold you **so high** that you feel like you're flying!

Some dads will help you
whatever you do.

tRUMP!

Some dads will trump
and then say it was you!

Some dads build magical castles of sand,

Or make you feel safe
just by holding
your hand.

Some dads drink soda
and give you a slurp,
And then laugh out loud
when you do a big burp!

Some dads look
BIG as a
GIANT to you,
And up on their
shoulders you feel
like one too!

Some dads get cross
and start sulking
and stamping,

GRRRRRRRR!

Just because they're a
bit rubbish at camping!

Some dads try hard but they really can't cook,

And some dads are
brilliant at reading a book.

Nobody's dad is like mine and I'm glad.

When I'm big I want to be

just

like

my

dad!